KIDS TV THEMES

easy playalong *for* flute

WISE PUBLICATIONS
part of The Music Sales Group
London/New York/Paris/Sydney/Copenhagen/Berlin/Madrid/Tokyo

For ease of play, the key and tempo of some of the themes in this book do not necessarily match editions of this title for other instruments. Such pieces, therefore, will not be suitable for group playing using different instruments.

Published by
Wise Publications
8/9 Frith Street,
London W1D 3JB, England.

Exclusive Distributors:
Music Sales Limited
Distribution Centre, Newmarket Road,
Bury St. Edmunds, Suffolk IP33 3YB, England.

Music Sales Pty Limited
120 Rothschild Avenue,
Rosebery, NSW 2018, Australia.

Order No. AM973566
ISBN 0-7119-9267-3

Music arranged by Simon Lesley.
Music processed by Enigma Music Production Services.
Cover photography courtesy George Taylor.
Printed in the United Kingdom by
Printwise (Haverhill) Limited, Haverhill, Suffolk.

CD recorded, mixed and mastered by Jonas Persson.
Instrumental solos by John Whelan.
Backing tracks arranged by Danny Gluckstein.

Captain Pugwash 6

Chatterhappy Ponies 10

Pingu 11

Pokemon Theme 12

Postman Pat 14

Roobarb & Custard 17

Rugrats 18

Sesame Street Theme 24

Sooty Theme 20

The Wombling Song 22

Flute Fingering Chart 4

Flute Fingering Chart

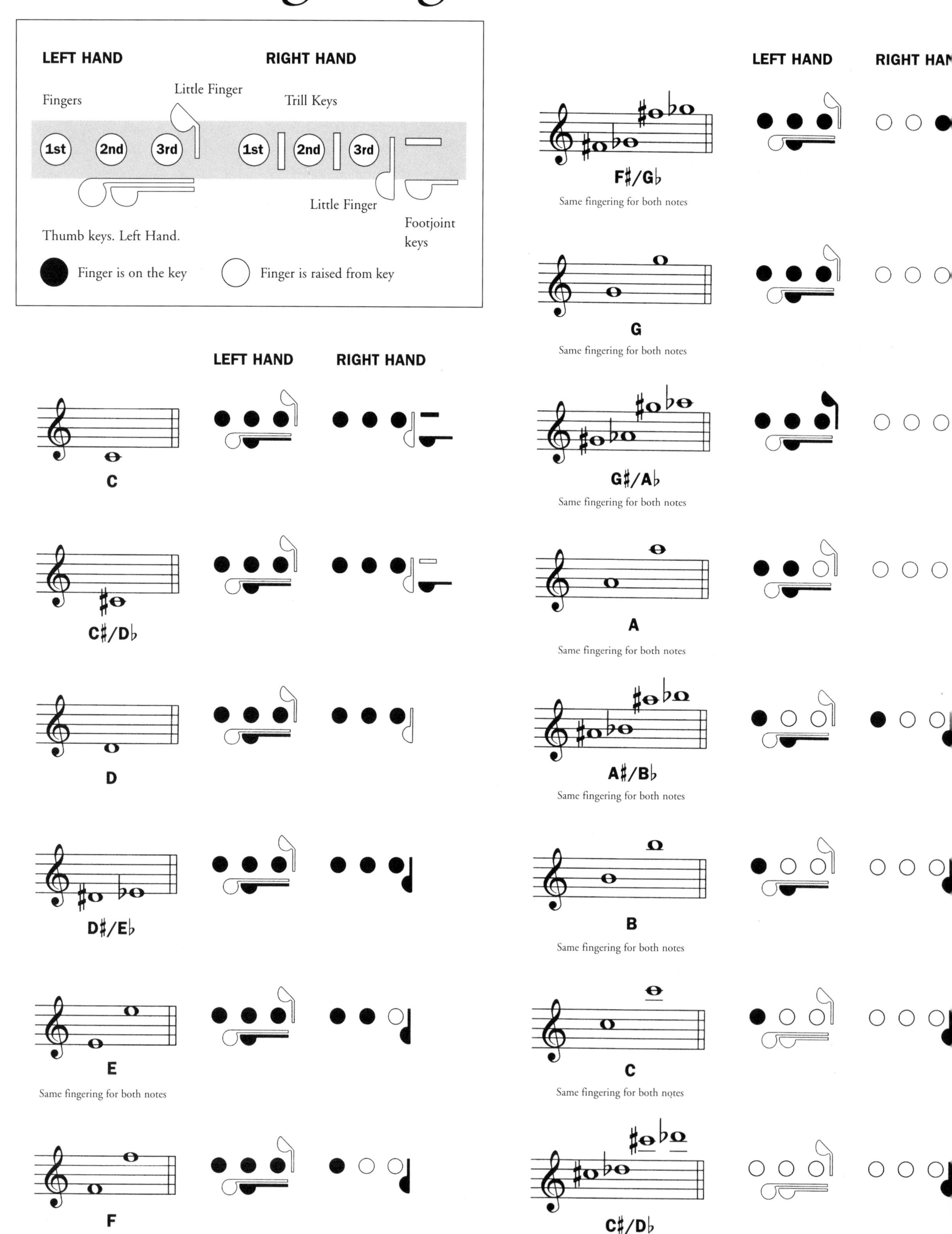

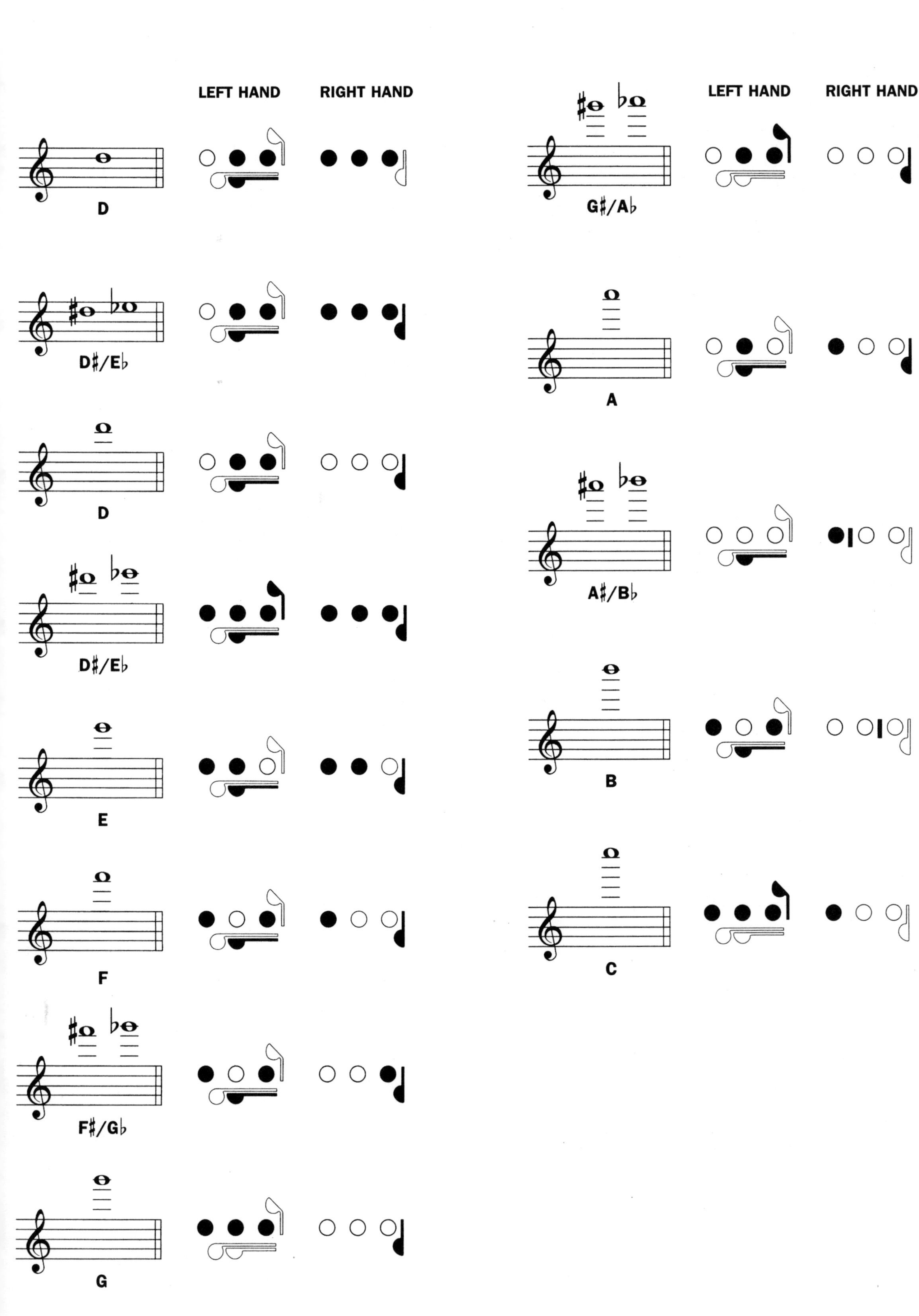
LEFT HAND
RIGHT HAND
D
D♯/E♭
D
D♯/E♭
E
F
F♯/G♭
G
LEFT HAND
RIGHT HAND
G♯/A♭
A
A♯/B♭
B
C

CAPTAIN PUGWASH

Traditional
Arranged by Gordon Lorenz

Lively sea-shanty ♩. = 170

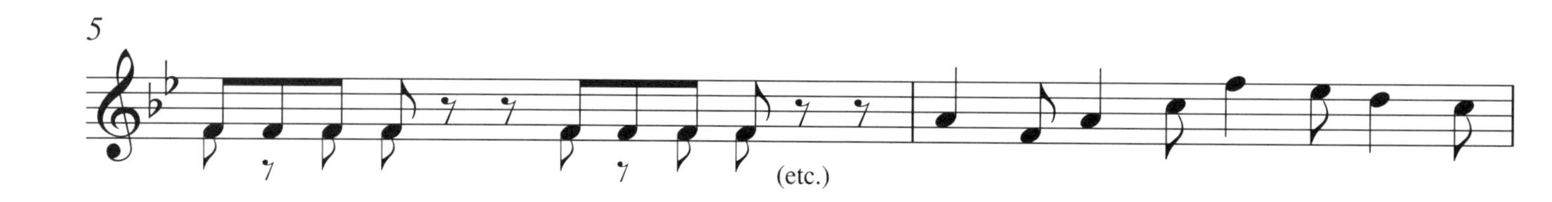

15
17
f
19
00:26
21
23
25
27
00:37
29

31
33
mf
35
00:48
37
39
41
43
01:00
45
47

49
f
51
01:11
53
55
57
59
01:22
61
63
65

CHATTERHAPPY PONIES

By Peter Gosling

PINGU

By Antonio Conde

POKEMON THEME

Words & Music by Tamara Loffler & John Siegler

35
ff
2
01:04
f
40
44
48
52
55
01:31
58
62
01:44
66
70
ff

POSTMAN PAT

Words & Music by Bryan Daly

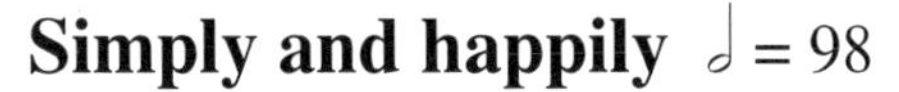

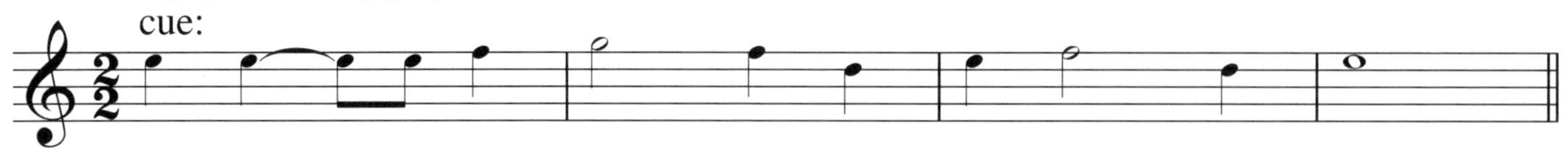

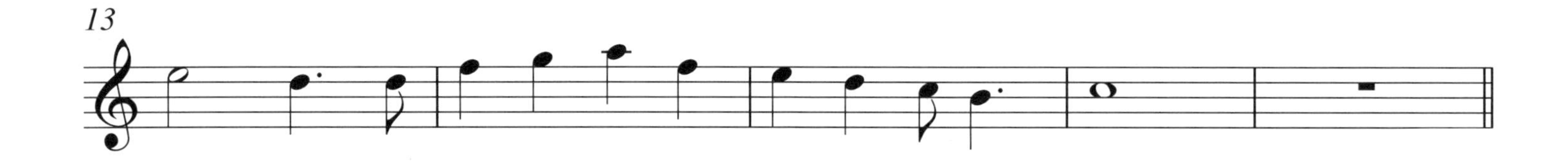

31
00:40
36
sub. p
41
Slower
a tempo
46
mp
50
54
01:17
59
Swung ♪'s
mf jazzier
63

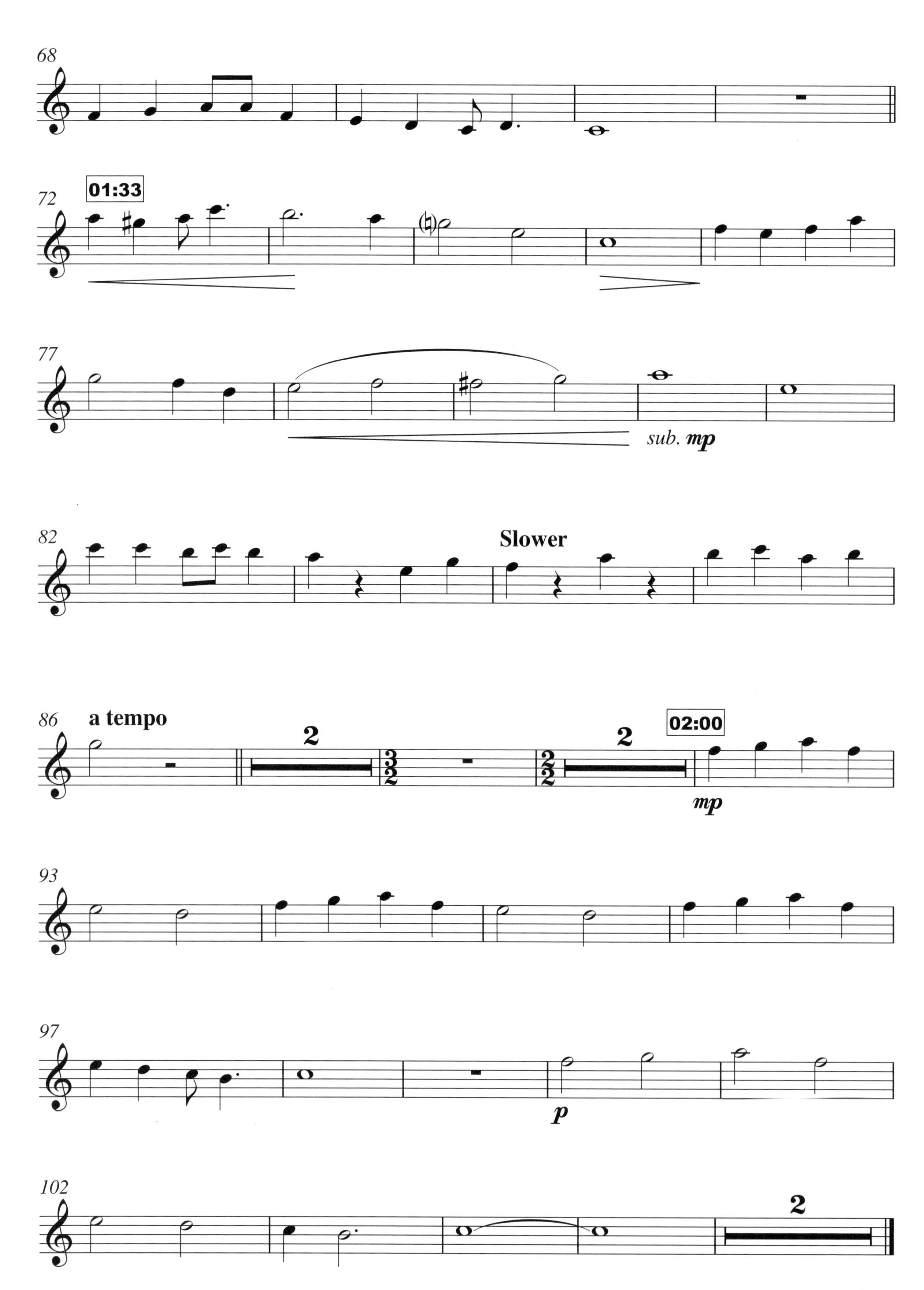
68
72
01:33
77
sub. mp
82
Slower
86
a tempo
2
2
02:00
mp
93
97
p
102
2

ROOBARB & CUSTARD

By Mark Pritchard & Johnny Hawksworth

RUGRATS

By Mark Mothersbaugh

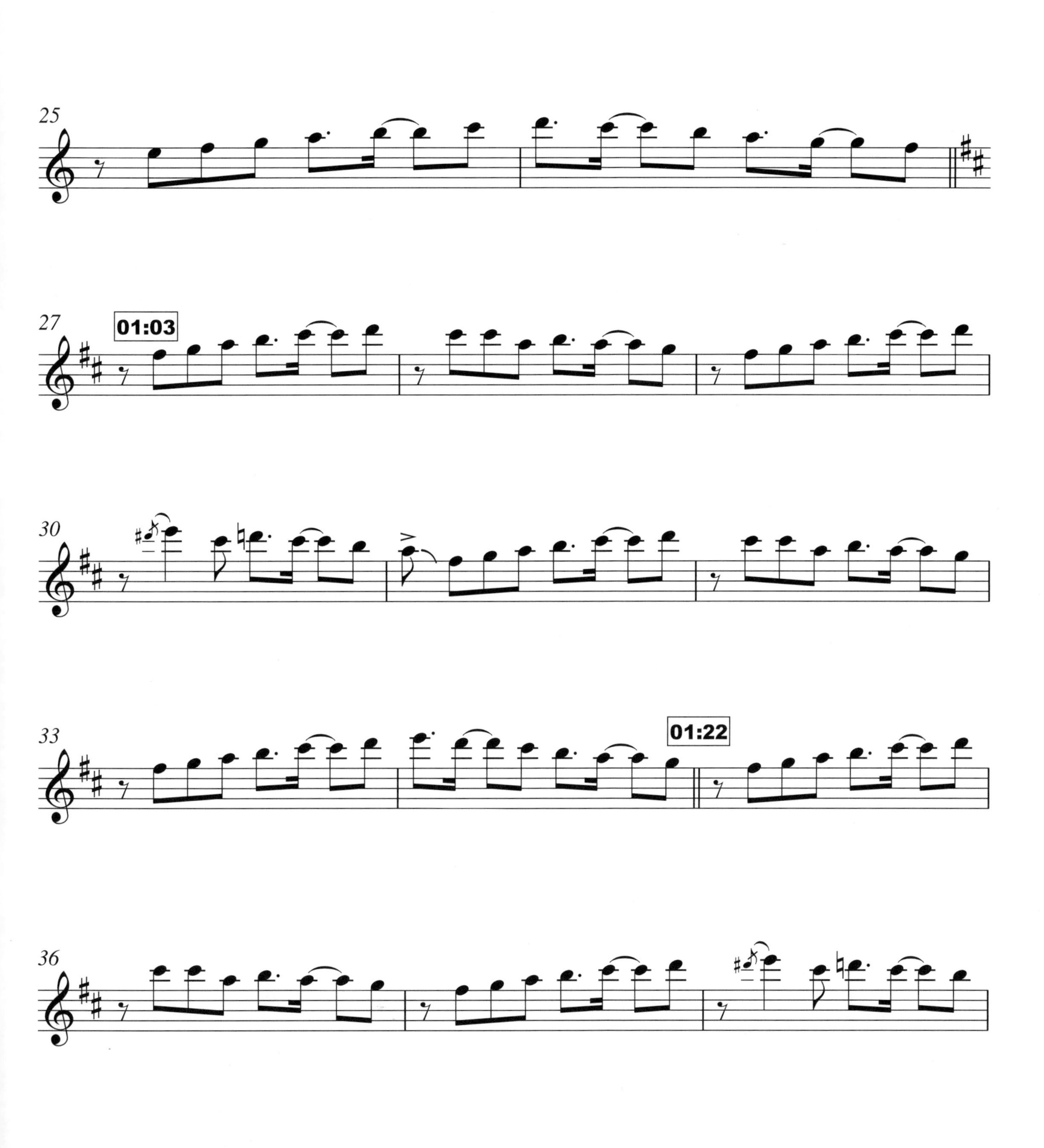
25
27
01:03
30
33
01:22
36

39
41

SOOTY THEME

By Harry Corbett

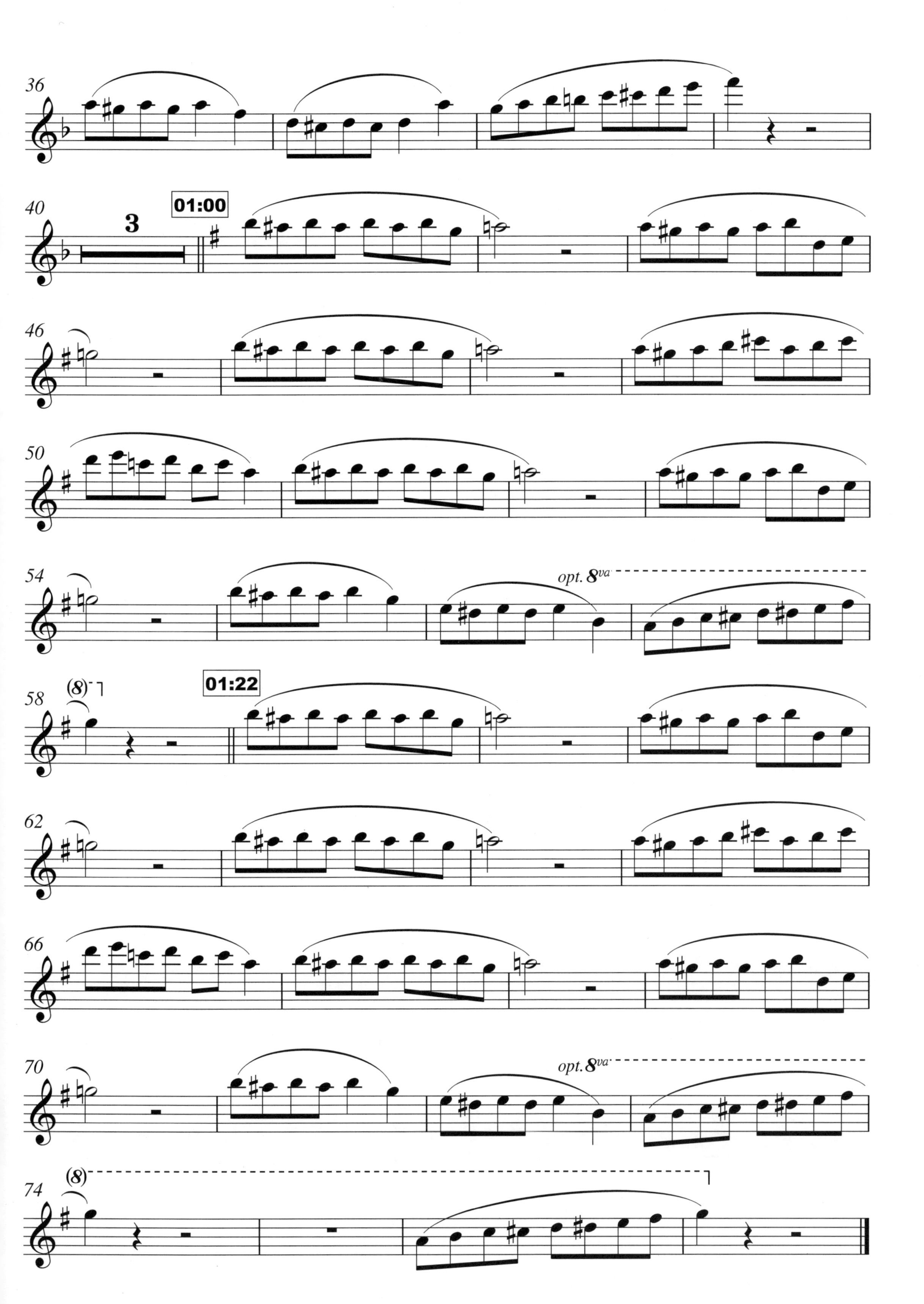
36
40
3
01:00
46
50
54
opt. 8va
58
(8)
01:22
62
66
70
opt. 8va
74
(8)

THE WOMBLING SONG

Words & Music by Mike Batt

25
29
00:52
mf
33
37
01:07
cresc.
41
f
45
3
01:26
mf
49
53

SESAME STREET THEME

Words & Music by Joe Raposo, Jon Stone & Bruce Hart